HUGLEIKUR DAGSSON

MY PUSSY
IS HUNGRY

ÓKEIBÆ

My Pussy is Hungry
© Hugleikur Dagsson 2013

Layout and cover design: Eyþór Páll Eyþórsson / Forlagið
Printing: Prentmiðlun / Poland

1st edition 2013
Reprinted 2014, 2016, 2017

Published in Reykjavík, UNESCO city of literature

Ókeibæ · Reykjavík · 2017

ISBN 978-9935-439-06-2

Ókeibæ is an imprint of ⬧ Forlagid ehf.
www.forlagid.is · www.okei.is

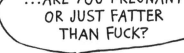

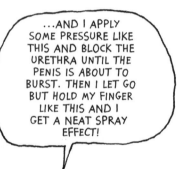

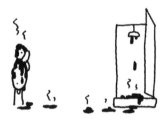

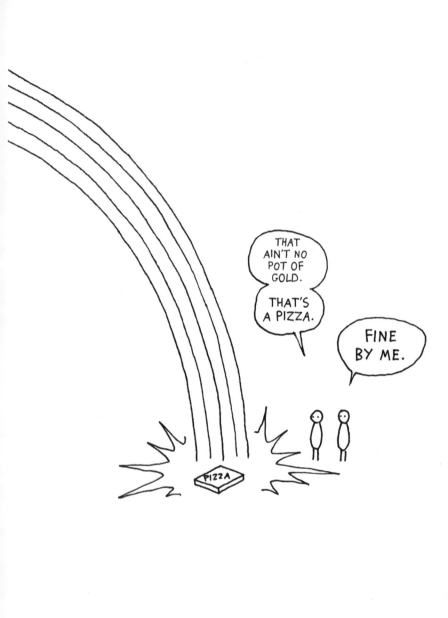

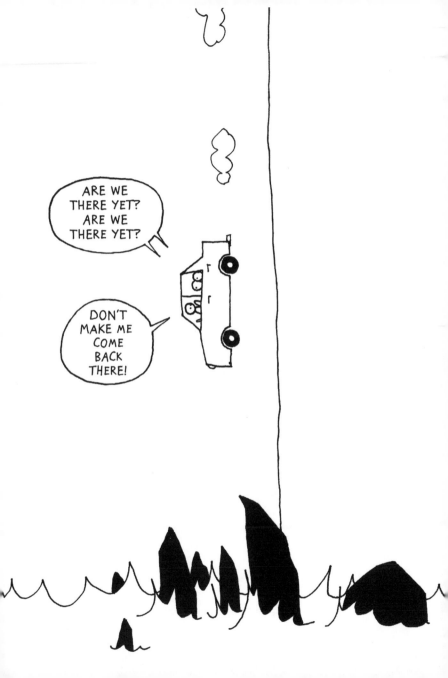

YOU'LL GET YOUR THUMB BACK AS SOON AS YOU PAY ME THE REST, MOM. IS THAT CLEAR?
YES, DEAR.
CHRYSTAL.

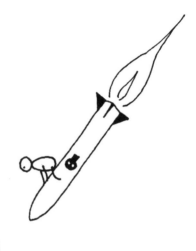

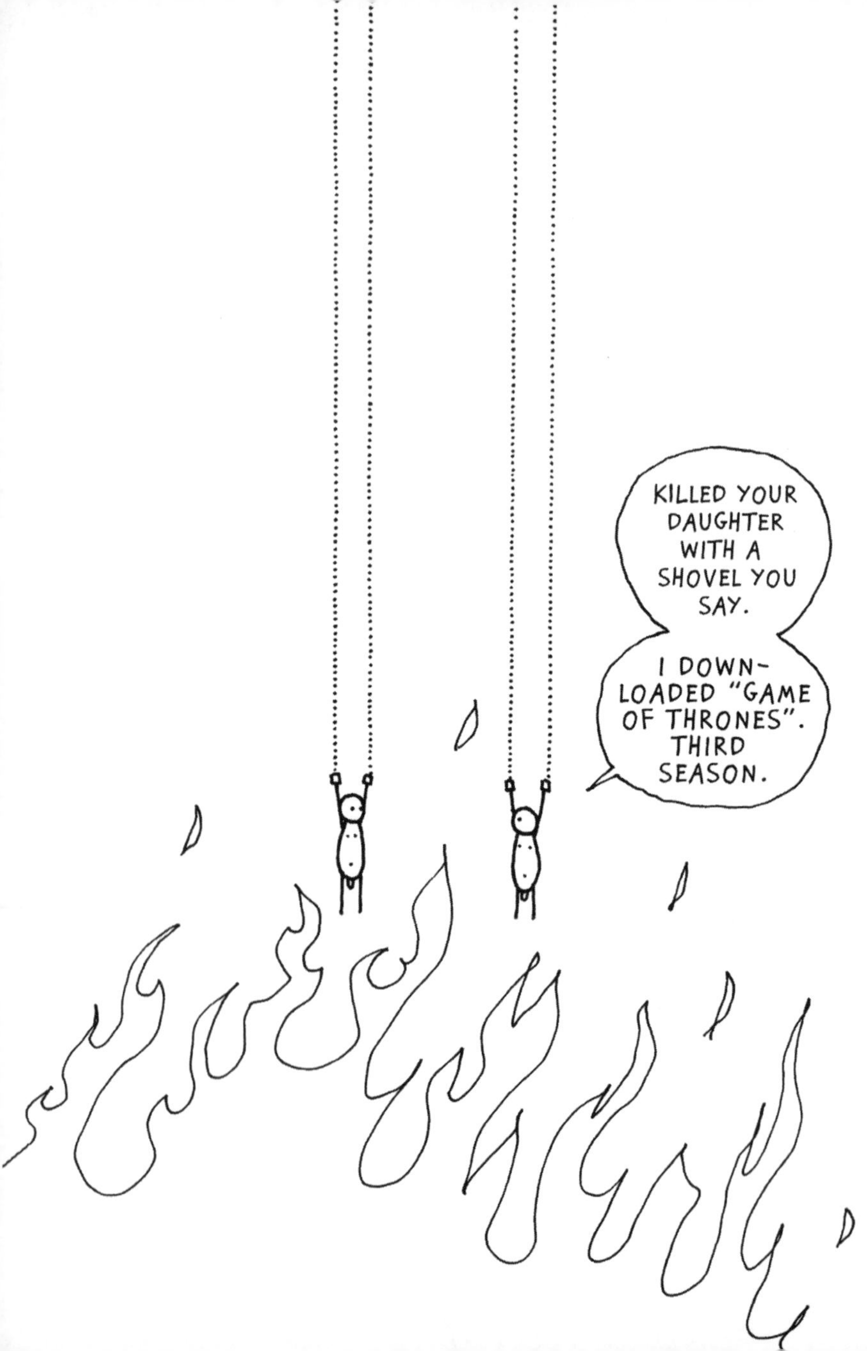
KILLED YOUR DAUGHTER WITH A SHOVEL YOU SAY.
I DOWN-LOADED "GAME OF THRONES". THIRD SEASON.

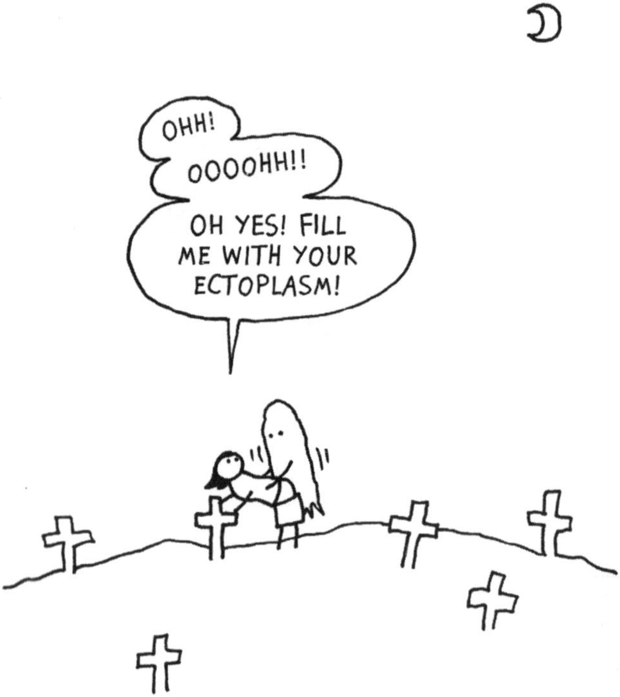
OHH!
OOOOHH!!
OH YES! FILL ME WITH YOUR ECTOPLASM!

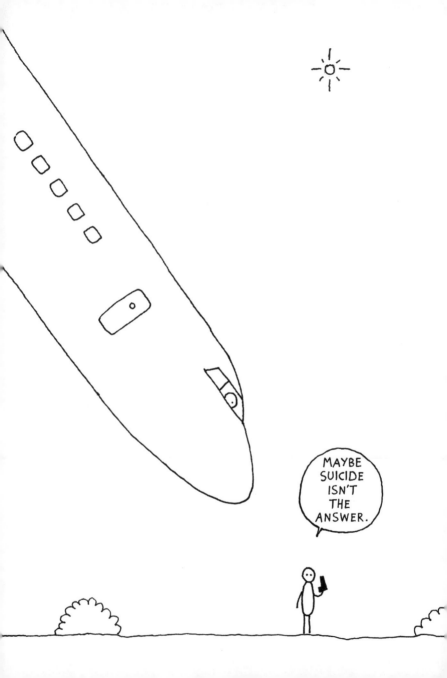

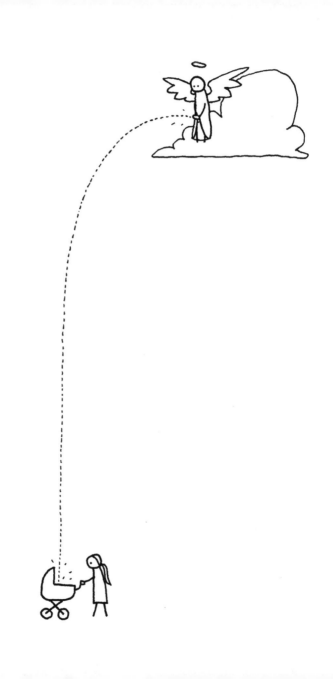

HI KIDS!
I'M KRUNCHIE,
KING OF KUKLUXIA,
AND THIS IS MY
SUPER UNICORN,
LOTTIE-5X.
UM...
...OKAY, BYE!

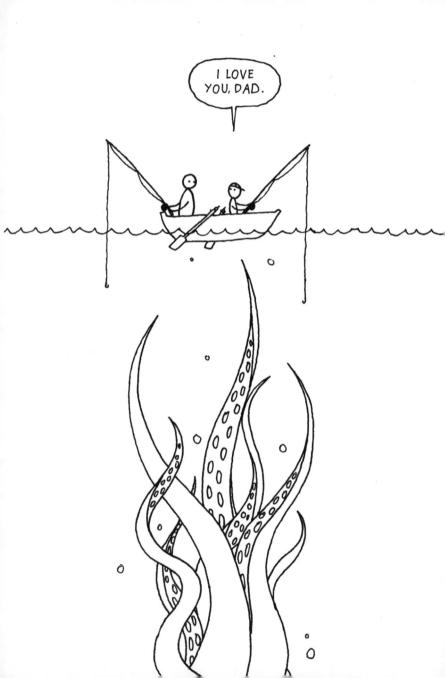

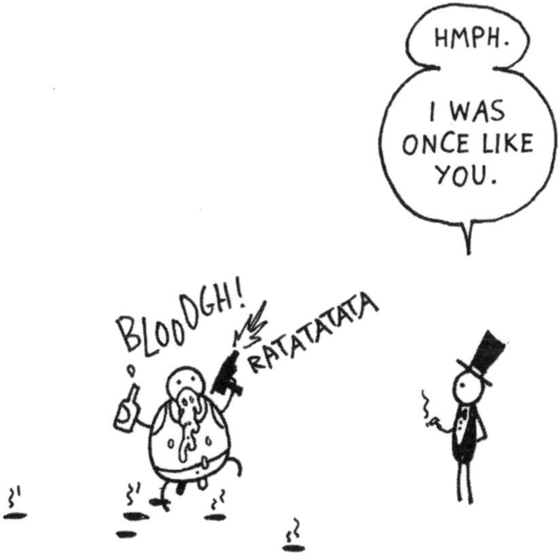
HMPH.
I WAS ONCE LIKE YOU.
BLOOOGH!
RATATATATA

DOMINO'S

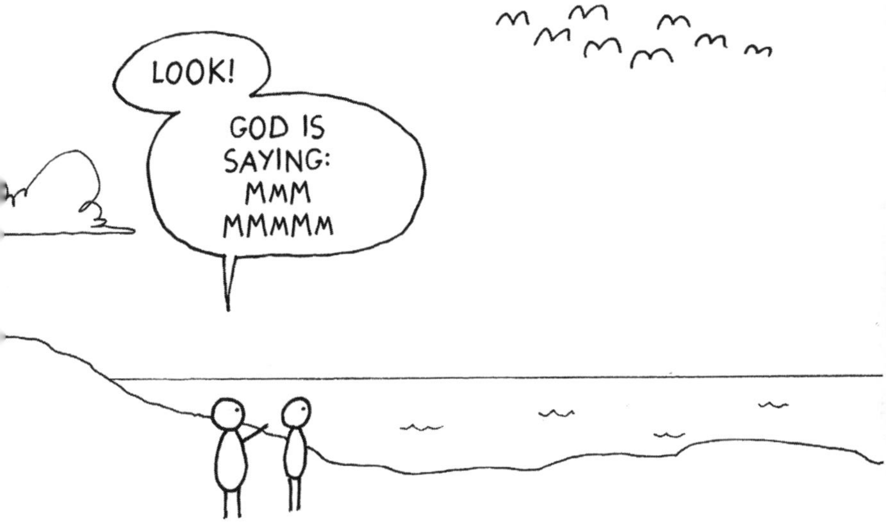
LOOK!
GOD IS SAYING: MMM MMMMM

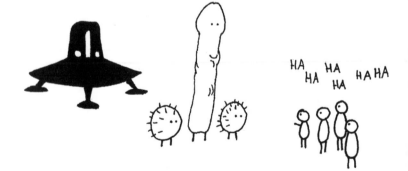